LENNY THE LIGHTHOUSE FINDS A DOLLAR

D1108856

Written by Dana Fennie

Illustrated by Bella Maher

Special thanks to Walter Blackmon for lighting the fire of enthusiasm
and giving me the inspiration to finally publish my little book.
Without Walt, I doubt I would have ever completed it.

Extra special thanks to Kenli, Amelia, and Georgia,
for my constant and ongoing motivation

"Wow a dollar!" shouted Lenny. "Is it my dollar?
What should I do with the dollar? I'm going to ask
everybody on the way home what I should do."

Lenny asked his
best friend Reddog,
"What do I do with this dollar?"

"Woof! I don't know anything
about dollars," barked Reddog.

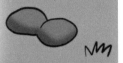

"You need to ask somebody
smarter than me."

As Thumper the cat looks hopefully at Lenny he said.
"You could buy me some cat food."

"But Thumper," cries Lenny, "I can see you just ate!"
"Oh Pashaw," grumbles Thumper. "I'm going to find some shade to relax in."

Lenny asks his friend McShip, "What should I do with the dollar?" McShip says, "Why, you can buy me some coal, so I can make steam and blow my whistle."

"But you blow your whistle all the time," moans Lenny,
"and it's really loud. I think I'll keep the dollar."
Lenny wasn't sure what to do with the dollar.
Was it even his dollar?

Lenny saw
Mrs. Sutterflower working in
her beautiful garden.

"Excuse me, Mrs.
Sutterflower," said Lenny.
"I found a dollar in the bushes
near the school.
What should I do with the
dollar I found?"

"Well," said Mrs.
Sutterflower, "If you found
the dollar, that means
someone lost the dollar. You
should try to find the person
who lost it. Maybe they need
the dollar."

"Oh boy!" shouts Lenny. "That's a great idea Mrs. Sutterflower! I'll see if I can find someone who lost a dollar."

"Excuse me Mr. Ryan, did you lose a dollar?" asked Lenny.
"No, I still have the dollar I had this morning,"
said Mr. Ryan. "Why don't you check with
Mr. Fennywhipple at the auto repair shop?"

Lenny told
Mr. Fennywhipple his story.
"Hmmm" Mr. Fennywhipple
said thoughtfully.

"Why don't you go ask Ol' Walter,
the lighthouse at Twinkle Beach?
He has been around for a long time,
He'll know the best thing to do."

Lenny has never talked with
Ol' Walter the Lighthouse.

Lenny has seen Ol' Walter
many times when he goes to
Twinkle Beach, but he has
always been a little afraid to
talk to Ol' Walter.

Lenny's mom always speaks
about how wise Ol' Walter is,
and how he has seen so much
over the years.

Ol' Walter always has good
thoughtful answers.

After dinner, Lenny asks his parents for permission to go see Ol' Walter after school. "As long as you're home in time to do your homework," said Lenny's mom. "Great! Thanks mom!" exclaims Lenny.

Lenny goes to bed and reads his favorite book.
Lenny likes imagining and dreaming about things.
Lenny will sit for hours on Twinkle Beach and think
about stuff he wants to do. Soon Lenny is asleep.

The next day after school, Lenny heads off to
Twinkle Beach to see Ol' Walter.

Ol' Walter stays up all night shining brightly for the ships, so he gets to sleep during the daytime.

Lenny sees Ol' Walter sleeping.
Very quietly Lenny calls out,
"Excuse me, Mr. Walter, Hello?"

"Who's there? Who's that?"
Ol' Walter said sleepily.

Very shyly Lenny says,
"My mom says you are very wise,
and if I have a problem you
might help me with it."

"Ho! Ho! Oh, she does, does
she?" replies Walter.

"Yes she does," said Lenny.

"Well, how about we introduce
ourselves first?" said Ol' Walter.
"That's the polite way to meet
someone new."

"That's right!" said Lenny.
"I'm Lenny the Lighthouse. I live in
town. I go to school and have a good
friend named Reddog, but he is not
with me today."

"Well," said Ol' Walter,
"I'm very glad to meet you Lenny. My
name is Walter and I live right here
on this bluff,
above Twinkle Beach."

"Now that we have introduced
ourselves, what is troubling my
new friend Lenny,
and how can I help?"

Lenny told Ol' Walter his story
about the dollar and how he did
not know if it was his dollar or
what he should do.

Ol' Walter listened patiently,
until Lenny was done.
Then he thought for a minute.

"Well," said Walter, "having money is a great responsibility, no matter how old you are. But you're right, first you have to find out who the dollar belongs to." Lenny asked, "How do I do that?"

"Here's what you can do." replied Ol' Walter. "Go to the police station and talk with Officer Ronnie. He will know what to do with the dollar. After that, make up some signs saying that you found a dollar. Put the signs up all around town. Always be sure to get permission before you put up your signs."

Officer Ronnie knew exactly what to do. He put the dollar in a safe at the police station, and gave Lenny a piece of paper saying he could come back in two weeks and claim the dollar.

The next day Lenny and Reddog went around the neighborhood putting up signs. He put one up in Mr. Ryan's store, and on Mrs. Sutterflower's mailbox. Lenny always asked for permission before he put up a sign.

Everyone wanted to help Lenny find the owner of the dollar.
Officer Ronnie even let them put
a sign up at the police station.

Meanwhile, Lenny and Reddog played together after school. Sometimes they went exploring in new places.

One day Lenny and Reddog were on their way to Twinkle
Beach. As they walked past the police station, Officer Ronnie
called to Lenny. "Hey Lenny, I have something for you!" Lenny
and Reddog looked at each other excitedly. "Oh boy!"
exclaimed Lenny. "Has the two weeks gone by already?"

"The dollar is yours," said Officer Ronnie. "You did the right thing Lenny. You found the dollar. You looked for the owner. You brought it to us, but nobody claimed it. So the dollar is yours! Congratulations Lenny!"

Lenny and Reddog were very happy and excited! As Lenny
and Reddog walked home, they thought of all the fun
things they could do with the dollar.

What would you do?

The End

Lessons that Lenny learned while he was looking for the owner of the dollar.

1. Honesty and good judgment: Lenny knew the dollar was not his. He knew he should not feed Thumper or buy McShip some coal. He knew he should do something besides just spend the dollar. He just didn't know what.

2. Look for answers: Lenny looked all over to try to find out what he should do with the dollar.

3. Always ask for permission: Lenny asked his mom before he went to see Ol' Walter. Lenny asked for permission before he put his signs up.

4. Introductions should always come first: Ol'Walter and Lenny introduced themselves first before they started talking.

5. Don't interrupt, and practice patience: Ol' Walter waited patiently for Lenny to finish his whole story before he answered Lenny.

6. Policemen are our friends: Officer Ronnie helped Lenny and Reddog.

7. Delayed Gratification: Lenny had to wait to get his dollar.

 Find the butterflies... I found 20, how many can you find?

Thank you for reading my little book! I truly hope you enjoyed it.
Dana

Watch for book 2...
When our friend Lenny decides what to do with his dollar.
It should be available by Christmas 2021.

Visit www.lennythelighthouse.com